English Progress Papers 1

Patrick Berry and Susan Hamlyn

Schofield&Sims

Introduction

The **English Progress Papers** provide structured activities that increase in difficulty throughout the series, developing your knowledge and skills in English. Use the series to prepare for school entrance examinations, to improve your English knowledge and to practise a range of English skills.

How to use this book

There are six papers in this book. Each contains 85 questions, worth up to 100 marks. A single paper may take between 45 and 75 minutes to complete, and you might need two or more sessions to complete one paper.

For exam preparation, revision and all-round practice, work through the papers in order. Ask an adult helper to mark each paper, correct mistakes and explain where you went wrong. To practise a topic that you find challenging, work through selected activities in order of difficulty using the **Topics chart**, which is free to download from the Schofield & Sims website.

What does each paper contain?

Each paper is divided into three parts. Work carefully through each one and do not rush.

The **English skills** questions focus on key areas of grammar, punctuation and spelling and help you to avoid common mistakes – in the use of apostrophes, for example. These questions will also expand your vocabulary, particularly if you incorporate the new words and phrases that you learn in to your own written work.

The multiple-choice **Comprehension** questions are not as easy as they look. Always read both the passage and the question carefully, particularly if all the answer options have some truth in them. One answer is always more accurate than the others, but careful thinking is needed to identify it.

The **Short writing task** is not designed as an extended piece of work and you will be able to complete some tasks in 20 to 30 minutes. Others may inspire you to write for longer – if you need more space, use separate sheets of paper. When working for a test or exam, restrict yourself to 30 minutes' writing, particularly in the last three months before the test. For ideas on how to tackle the different kinds of task, see **Short writing task tips**, which is free to download from the Schofield & Sims website.

Answers

The adult who is helping you will use the pull-out answer booklet to mark your work. If you get some questions wrong, check your answers against the correct answers given. Take time, with a dictionary and/or with an adult, to learn and remember why the answer given is correct. When checking a comprehension question, re-read carefully both the passage and the question and carefully think it through.

Use the **Progress chart** at the back of this book to record your marks and measure progress.

Downloads

Free downloads are available from the Schofield & Sims website (www.schofieldandsims.co.uk/free-downloads), including the resources mentioned above, extra practice material, guidance on alternative spellings and a glossary of English skills vocabulary.

Published by **Schofield & Sims Ltd**,
7 Mariner Court, Wakefield, West Yorkshire WF4 3FL, UK
Telephone 01484 607080
www.schofieldandsims.co.uk

First published in 1993
This edition copyright © Schofield & Sims Ltd, 2018
Third impression 2019

Authors: **Patrick Berry and Susan Hamlyn**
Patrick Berry and Susan Hamlyn have asserted their moral rights under the Copyright, Designs and Patents Act, 1988, to be identified as the authors of this work.

Grateful thanks to the Head and Year 6 pupils of Notting Hill and Ealing Junior School (GDST) for trialling **English Progress Papers** in their school.

British Library Cataloguing in Publication Data
A catalogue record for this book is available from the British Library.

Design by **Ledgard Jepson Ltd**

Printed in the UK by **Page Bros (Norwich) Ltd**

ISBN 978 07217 1473 8

Contents

Note for parents, tutors, teachers and other adult helpers

A pull-out answers section (pages A1 to A12) appears in the centre of this book, between pages 26 and 27 (Paper 3). This provides answers to all the **English skills** and **Comprehension** questions, as well as guidelines for marking the **Short writing tasks**. It also gives simple guidance on how best to use this book. Remove the pull-out section before the child begins working through the practice papers.

You may wish the child to have access to a dictionary – either while he or she is working through the papers or after you have marked them. Make a decision on this before the child begins work. You may also give the child some separate sheets of lined paper for continuing the **Short writing task** if needed.

Paper 1

START HERE

Q. 1–60 English skills

MARK

Q. 1–5
punctuation

Rewrite the sentence correctly, adding the necessary punctuation. Put in capital letters, speech marks, commas, apostrophes and full stops.

megan wont be at school in the morning because shell be going to the dentist mrs brown explained to the teacher

____

____

____

____

1–5 ☐ 5

Q. 6–10
nouns

Add to the sentence a noun that is made from the word shown in capitals.

6 HIGH The balloon soared to a great ____________________. — 6 ☐ 1

7 RECEIVE Make sure you get a ____________________ for your money. — 7 ☐ 1

8 MARRY Their ____________________ will take place next year in May. — 8 ☐ 1

9 ABLE I'm not sure I have the ____________________ to do this job. — 9 ☐ 1

10 STRONG Lifting this box will take all my ____________________. — 10 ☐ 1

Q. 11–15
word choice

Three words appear in brackets. Underline the *one* word that completes the sentence correctly.

11 There is the boy (who, whose, whom) gave me the book. — 11 ☐ 1

12 (Who, Whom, Whose) have you come to see? — 12 ☐ 1

13 I have come to see (there, they're, their) father. — 13 ☐ 1

14 We (lied, layed, lay) down on the soft grass. — 14 ☐ 1

15 To become an expert you must (practice, practise) every day. — 15 ☐ 1

MARK ☐

English skills

MARK

Q. 16–20
word meanings, synonyms

Underline the *one* word that is closest in meaning to the word shown in capitals.

							Mark
16	CELEBRATED	green,	persevere,	clamour,	poor,	famous	16 ☐ 1
17	LETHAL	ugly,	dangerous,	delicious,	greedy,	tiny	17 ☐ 1
18	ACCURATE	fiddly,	kind,	healthy,	exact,	small	18 ☐ 1
19	DONATE	lose,	strive,	give,	secrete,	please	19 ☐ 1
20	LIVID	dead,	false,	innocent,	murky,	angry	20 ☐ 1

Q. 21–25
indirect to direct speech

Change the sentence from indirect (reported) speech to direct speech.
For example, *Dr Jones suggested I rest my ankle till the swelling went down* becomes *"Do rest that ankle till the swelling goes down," suggested Dr Jones.*

21 The teacher said I had to re-do my homework.

____ 21 ☐ 1

22 Mum asked why we were so late getting home.

____ 22 ☐ 1

23 George told Harry he was sorry for what he had done.

____ 23 ☐ 1

24 The student said he was sick of doing exams.

____ 24 ☐ 1

25 My gran told me my laces were undone – again!

____ 25 ☐ 1

Q. 26–30
apostrophes for possession, plurals

Change the singular word(s) to plural. If an apostrophe is used, make sure that you put it in the correct position.
For example, *the lady's dog* becomes *the ladies' dogs.*

26 the man's shoe _______________________ 26 ☐ 1

27 my sister-in-law _______________________ 27 ☐ 1

28 his mother's birthday _______________________ 28 ☐ 1

29 man, woman and child _______________________ 29 ☐ 1

30 the dictionary's definition _______________________ 30 ☐ 1

MARK ☐

English skills

MARK

Q. 31–35
spelling

Write out the sentence, correcting any misspellings.

31 It was the most intresting film we'd ever scene.

___________________________ 31 [ ] 1

32 You'll probaly miss youre train if you don't hurry.

___________________________ 32 [ ] 1

33 He'd groan so much I didn't reconise him.

___________________________ 33 [ ] 1

34 Sanjay apoligised so sincerly that he was let of.

___________________________ 34 [ ] 1

35 Did you recieve the present? I scent it first class.

___________________________ 35 [ ] 1

Q. 36–40
abbreviations

Write the words that the abbreviation (shortened form) stands for.

36 EU ___________________________ 36 [ ] 1

37 www ___________________________ 37 [ ] 1

38 PS ___________________________ 38 [ ] 1

39 NB ___________________________ 39 [ ] 1

40 a.m. (as in 11.30 a.m.) ___________________________ 40 [ ] 1

Q. 41–45
alphabetical order

Put the words in alphabetical order by writing the numbers from 1 to 5 in the brackets.

41 colour (____), cord (____), colt (____), corridor (____), cooler (____) 41 [ ] 1

42 drip (____), dreary (____), dragon (____), drink (____), dragging (____) 42 [ ] 1

43 felt (____), ferry (____), fence (____), feel (____), fetch (____) 43 [ ] 1

44 psalm (____), pheasant (____), pseudo (____), philately (____), psychiatrist (____) 44 [ ] 1

45 eyrie (____), eerie (____), eeriness (____), ear (____), eerily (____) 45 [ ] 1

MARK [ ]

English skills

MARK

Q. 46–50

antonyms

Write down the antonym (opposite) of the word.

			MARK
46	temporary	____________	46 ☐ 1
47	arrival	____________	47 ☐ 1
48	transparent	____________	48 ☐ 1
49	generous	____________	49 ☐ 1
50	expand	____________	50 ☐ 1

Q. 51–55

comparative and superlative

Using the example as a guide, write the comparative and superlative of the adjective given. You may need to use more than one word.

	ADJECTIVE	COMPARATIVE	SUPERLATIVE	MARK
Example:	FINE	*finer*	*finest*	
51	WEAK	____________	____________	51 ☐ 1
52	HEALTHY	____________	____________	52 ☐ 1
53	HOPEFUL	____________	____________	53 ☐ 1
54	SMALL	____________	____________	54 ☐ 1
55	KINDLY	____________	____________	55 ☐ 1

Q. 56–60

apostrophes for abbreviation

Abbreviate (shorten) the phrase by using an apostrophe.
For example, *They are not coming* becomes *They're not coming.*

			MARK
56	one of the clock	____________	56 ☐ 1
57	he will not	____________	57 ☐ 1
58	they do not	____________	58 ☐ 1
59	Is she not going?	____________	59 ☐ 1
60	Where have you put my coat?	____________	60 ☐ 1

MARK ☐

ENGLISH SKILLS SUB-TOTAL ☐ 60

Q. 61–75 Comprehension

MARK

Read this passage carefully.

Fearsome Monster or Noble Beast?

A brief introduction to the dragon as seen by different cultures.

What do you think of when you picture a dragon? A fire-breathing, winged and tailed, scaly monster? A terrifying creature that imprisons princesses and guards great hoards of treasure? A noble and 5 fantastic beast with great strength? Or a hapless victim of a gallant knight who thrusts a spear down its throat?

You will doubtless have seen pictures of dragons and will know stories about their doings. All 10 countries and cultures have their own dragon myths and legends. Some see their beasts as snake-like. Others imagine them as marine creatures, emerging from the seas to terrify – or to save – as the mood takes them. In China, dragons are seen as powerful 15 and important. Dragons in the Slavic countries are many-headed and Turkish dragons breathe fire – not through their mouths but from their tails!

But the Welsh have a rather different view of their fabulous monster. They even have a bright 20 red dragon on their national flag. True, the Welsh red dragon is as fearsome as similar beasts found elsewhere – with its long forked tongue and fiery looks – but the Welsh people are very proud of their 25 dragon and he appears everywhere. You will find him on every local council's signs and headed paper, on documents, on sports' clubs badges, in arts centres, choirs' programmes and even on stamps!

Stories of the famous red Welsh dragon go far back 30 in history. In some myths he is seen as the symbol of the brave Welsh, whereas the invading Saxons are depicted as a white dragon. The story is linked to the father of the great King Arthur and his Knights of the Round Table. King Arthur's father was Uther 35 Pendragon – 'Pen' meaning 'head' or 'chief' – so his name meant, mysteriously, 'Uther Chief Dragon'! A famous early historian tells us that this was because Uther saw a dragon-shaped comet one night and, taking this as a good omen for the 40 coming battle, had one embroidered on his standard – the flag carried before his armies.

Now read these questions. You have a choice of four answers to each question. Choose the *one* answer you think the best. Draw a line in the box next to its letter, like this.

A [—]

61 Which word best describes our views of dragons?

A various
B identical
C dangerous
D imaginary

A ☐ B ☐ C ☐ D ☐

61 2

62 From what source or sources do we learn about dragons?

A history
B art
C legends and myths
D television

A ☐ B ☐ C ☐ D ☐

62 2

MARK

Comprehension

MARK

63 Which word best describes the meaning of the word 'hapless' (line 5)?

A cheerful
B miserable
C unfortunate
D cowardly

A ☐ B ☐ C ☐ D ☐

63 ☐ 2

64 Which word is similar in meaning to 'legend' (line 11)?

A fable
B tradition
C picture
D history

A ☐ B ☐ C ☐ D ☐

64 ☐ 2

65 What is the meaning of 'marine' (line 12)?

A swimming
B amphibious
C evil
D living in the sea

A ☐ B ☐ C ☐ D ☐

65 ☐ 2

66 'Fabulous' (line 19) comes from the noun 'fable'. What does this suggest about dragons?

A that they are not real
B that they are very exciting
C that they are popular
D that they are scary

A ☐ B ☐ C ☐ D ☐

66 ☐ 2

67 Which of the following statements is *not* true?

A Welsh dragons look intimidating.
B The red dragon is a popular symbol in Wales.
C The Welsh are ashamed of their dragon.
D It is not difficult to spot a red dragon in Wales.

A ☐ B ☐ C ☐ D ☐

67 ☐ 2

68 Who were the Saxons?

A people who wanted to take over Welsh territory
B white dragons
C mythical people who liked fighting
D people who hid inside a white dragon

A ☐ B ☐ C ☐ D ☐

68 ☐ 2

MARK ☐

Comprehension

MARK

69 Why did Uther have a dragon on his standard?

A because he thought it would frighten the enemy
B because he wanted a dragon-shaped comet
C because he was going into battle
D because he thought it was a lucky sign

A ☐ B ☐ C ☐ D ☐

69 ☐ 2

70 Which of the phrases below would best complete the sentence?

The writer finds stories of dragons ______________________.

A frightening and dangerous
B fascinating and colourful
C random and weird
D complicated and old-fashioned

A ☐ B ☐ C ☐ D ☐

70 ☐ 2

71 Some people may view the dragon as a 'terrifying creature that imprisons princesses and guards great hoards of treasure' (lines 3–4).
Which of the following words is used in the extract as a verb?

A terrifying
B hoards
C creature
D guards

A ☐ B ☐ C ☐ D ☐

71 ☐ 2

Find the spelling mistake. Underline it and write the box letter at the end of the line.

72

Dragonology	is the official	sceintific name	for dragon studies.	
A	B	C	D	☐

72 ☐ 2

73

There are numerous	mysterious	mythalogical	creatures.	
A	B	C	D	☐

73 ☐ 2

74

The people of	Whales regard	the dragon as their	national mascot.	
A	B	C	D	☐

74 ☐ 2

75

Dragons probably	never actually	existed exept	in our imagination.	
A	B	C	D	☐

75 ☐ 2

MARK ☐

COMPREHENSION SUB-TOTAL ☐ 30

Q. 76–85 Short writing task

MARK

Write for 20–30 minutes on *one* of the following. Continue on a separate sheet if you need to.

a) You have discovered a baby dragon. Describe it in detail.

b) Treasure!

c) Do you enjoy myths and legends? How important do you think they are?

END OF TEST

SHORT WRITING TASK SUB-TOTAL		10
English skills sub-total (from page 7)		60
Comprehension sub-total (from page 10)		30
Short writing task sub-total (from this page)		10
PAPER 1 TOTAL MARK		100

START HERE

Q. 1–60 English skills

MARK

Q. 1–5
punctuation

Rewrite the sentence correctly, adding the necessary punctuation.

im very sorry dr kumar isnt here at the moment said the receptionist but hell be back soon

____

____

____

____

1–5 5

Q. 6–10
nouns

Add to the sentence a noun that is made from the word shown in capitals.

6 GRAND They were awestruck by the ______________ of the view. 6 1

7 SUCCEED Sandip enjoyed his ______________ in the contest. 7 1

8 CURIOUS The proverb says that ______________ killed the cat. 8 1

9 LAZY Ava's constant ______________ lost her the job. 9 1

10 MUSICAL The ______________ played the piece well. 10 1

Q. 11–15
homonyms

Write the *one* word that has *both* meanings.

In one of these items, the word is pronounced differently depending on the meaning.

11 small new plant / to fire a gun ______________ 11 1

12 unit of time / very tiny indeed ______________ 12 1

13 quick lowering of the head / aquatic bird ______________ 13 1

14 short period of time / magic formula ______________ 14 1

15 strong- and spicy-tasting root / reddish orange colour ______________ 15 1

MARK

English skills

MARK

Q. 16–20 word choice

Two words appear in brackets. Underline the *one* word that completes the sentence correctly.

16 The speaker talked about (current, currant) affairs. 16 ☐ 1

17 He (swim, swam, swum) across the river. 17 ☐ 1

18 The (principal, principle) addressed the school. 18 ☐ 1

19 None of us (are, is, am) going out today. 19 ☐ 1

20 Can you (prophecy, prophesy) what will happen? 20 ☐ 1

Q. 21–25 parts of speech, nouns, adjectives, adverbs, verbs

Read the sentence. Decide whether the underlined word is a noun, an adjective, an adverb or a verb. Write your answer on the line.

21 I haven't packed much – my backpack is light. ________ 21 ☐ 1

22 I can't talk now so I'll call you later. ________ 22 ☐ 1

23 Please finish your practice before the film starts. ________ 23 ☐ 1

24 I asked her the time but she couldn't advise me. ________ 24 ☐ 1

25 My cat's favourite toy is his squeaky mouse. ________ 25 ☐ 1

Q. 26–30 comparative and superlative

Using the example as a guide, write the comparative and superlative of the adjective given. You may need to use more than one word.

	ADJECTIVE	COMPARATIVE	SUPERLATIVE	
Example:	ROUGH	*rougher*	*roughest*	
26	LITTLE	________	________	26 ☐ 1
27	BAD	________	________	27 ☐ 1
28	THOUGHTFUL	________	________	28 ☐ 1
29	TINY	________	________	29 ☐ 1
30	THIN	________	________	30 ☐ 1

MARK ☐

English skills

MARK

Q. 31–35
past tense

Add to the sentence the past tense of the verb shown in capitals.

31 CREEP I have ______________________ into the cellar. — 31 | 1

32 EAT I have ______________________ your dinner. — 32 | 1

33 SING I have ______________________ in the concert. — 33 | 1

34 FIGHT I have ______________________ against the bullies. — 34 | 1

35 SPEAK I have ______________________ up for her. — 35 | 1

Q. 36–40
grammar, spelling

Write out the sentence, correcting any errors.

36 This is the best of the two games.

____ — 36 | 1

37 Each of the girls had their doll.

____ — 37 | 1

38 We new she had broke her leg.

____ — 38 | 1

39 We couldn't answer none of the questions.

____ — 39 | 1

40 Neither of them were hurt in the accident.

____ — 40 | 1

Q. 41–45
direct to indirect speech

Change the sentence from direct to indirect (reported) speech.

41 "Where have you been?" Mum asked Kassim.

____ — 41 | 1

42 "I don't feel very well," said Tom.

____ — 42 | 1

43 "It's time I went to school," replied Zofia.

____ — 43 | 1

44 "How far is it to Leeds?" Sam asked the attendant.

____ — 44 | 1

45 "It's only about 10 miles," he replied.

____ — 45 | 1

MARK

English skills

MARK

Q. 46–50 spelling

Read the clue. Fill in the missing letters to make the word.

46	somewhere to live	a ___ ___ ___ ___ m ___ ___ ___ ___ ___ ___ n	46 ☐ 1
47	to own	p ___ ___ ___ ___ ___ ___	47 ☐ 1
48	a happening	o ___ ___ ___ r ___ ___ ___ ___ ___	48 ☐ 1
49	to make someone blush	e ___ ___ ___ ___ ___ ___ ___ ___	49 ☐ 1
50	at once	i ___ ___ ___ ___ ___ ___ ___ ___ ___ y	50 ☐ 1

Q. 51–55 adverbs, suffixes

Add *ly* to the adjective to turn it into an adverb, making any changes needed as you do so.

51	happy	____________________	51 ☐ 1
52	helpful	____________________	52 ☐ 1
53	casual	____________________	53 ☐ 1
54	wise	____________________	54 ☐ 1
55	fine	____________________	55 ☐ 1

Q. 56–60 apostrophes for abbreviation

Abbreviate (shorten) the phrase by using an apostrophe.
For example, *Will she not do it?* becomes *Won't she do it?*

56	You will eat later.	________________________________	56 ☐ 1
57	Who has gone out?	________________________________	57 ☐ 1
58	I have had enough.	________________________________	58 ☐ 1
59	We cannot find it.	________________________________	59 ☐ 1
60	All is well that ends well.	________________________________	60 ☐ 1

MARK ☐

ENGLISH SKILLS SUB-TOTAL ☐ 60

Q. 61–75 Comprehension

MARK

Read this passage carefully.

My Big Day

Ahmad does his best to measure up.

There were about 15 kids there when we arrived. I had been panicking about being late on this Big Day but the bus, which seemed to have yawned along the way and snoozed at every stop, woke up and almost galloped for the last half mile. Dad and I jumped off and ran to 171 High Street. I had expected a glossy studio but the door was ancient and peeling, the hallway was dark and smelled of old dinners and 5 the room into which we all crowded was dim and didn't have enough chairs. The girl who let us in wore weird black eye make-up and heels as high as a crane. She said her name was something that sounded like Mush. Some of the kids looked really nervous. One or two were practising their audition pieces, oblivious to everyone else in the room. Most of them were in jeans and hoodies, but a few dressed seriously cool as if they spent their lives on film sets and lunching with stars. I felt a bit embarrassed 10 about my trainers.

Mush called us away, one by one, to be auditioned. I breathed deeply and slowly as I had learned to do – ever since my first part in the school play, when I nearly died of nerves. It helped. I repeated my speech to myself with all the pauses and emphases in the right places. It was good. I knew I was good. I really wanted this part. I wanted to pay Dad back for all the work he'd done for me – getting me drama 15 lessons, taking a day off work to take me to the audition, persuading school to let me go. I wanted to make him proud of me. And I knew I could do it.

Suddenly – there it was – my name! I followed Mush down a corridor into a large room with three men and a woman sitting behind a long table. The woman looked up and said hello. Then the middle man looked up and frowned. He stared hard at me.

20 "How tall are you?" he asked.

"I'm 1.6 metres," I said, trembling slightly.

The man looked at the woman and I thought I saw him shake his head.

"I'm so sorry," she said. "That's just a bit too tall for this part. They should have told you."

Now read these questions. You have a choice of four answers to each question. Choose the *one* answer you think the best. Draw a line in the box next to its letter, like this.

A [—]

61 What does this passage describe?

A taking part in a journey
B taking part in a film
C taking part in an audition
D taking part in a fashion show

A [ ] B [ ] C [ ] D [ ]

61 2

62 How is the bus described?

A as if it were old and broken down
B as if it were a sleepy animal
C as being late and slow
D as being very excitable

A [ ] B [ ] C [ ] D [ ]

62 2

MARK

Comprehension

MARK

63 Which of the following phrases best describes 171 High Street?

A smart and modern
B crowded and unfriendly
C noisy and brightly-lit
D dilapidated and musty

A ☐ B ☐ C ☐ D ☐

63 ☐ 2

64 Which of these is another word for 'audition'?

A rehearsal
B speech
C try-out
D exam

A ☐ B ☐ C ☐ D ☐

64 ☐ 2

65 We are told that Mush wears 'heels as high as a crane' (line 6). Of what kind of writing is this an example?

A exaggeration
B metaphor
C measurement
D simile

A ☐ B ☐ C ☐ D ☐

65 ☐ 2

66 Some of the girls and boys were 'oblivious to everyone else in the room' (line 8). What does this mean?

A They were trying to impress the others.
B They were taking no notice of the others.
C They were noisier than the others.
D They were cleverer than the others.

A ☐ B ☐ C ☐ D ☐

66 ☐ 2

67 How does Ahmad, the narrator, feel by the end of the second paragraph?

A unprepared and frightened
B nervous and worried
C excited and proud
D calm and confident

A ☐ B ☐ C ☐ D ☐

67 ☐ 2

68 Which of the words below would best complete the sentence?

Ahmad feels a great deal of ________________ to his father.

A gratitude
B concern
C hopefulness
D generosity

A ☐ B ☐ C ☐ D ☐

68 ☐ 2

MARK ☐

Comprehension

MARK

69 The narrator has experienced several emotions during this extract. Which *two* of the following do you think might best describe his feelings by the end of the passage?

1. nervousness 2. disappointment 3. anger 4. disapproval

A 2 and 3 only
B 1 and 4 only
C 2 and 4 only
D 1 and 3 only

A ☐ B ☐ C ☐ D ☐

69 2

70 Think about how Ahmad might have felt after the audition. Which of the phrases below would best complete the sentence?

The boy in the story felt ________________ on account of his height.

A not selected
B discriminated against
C impolitely ignored
D disallowed

A ☐ B ☐ C ☐ D ☐

70 2

71 Which of the following best describes the words 'High Street' (line 3) and 'Mush' (line 7).

A common nouns
B adjectives
C verbs
D proper nouns

A ☐ B ☐ C ☐ D ☐

71 2

Find the spelling mistake. Underline it and write the box letter at the end of the line.

	A	B	C	D	
72	There are usally	far more people	auditioning than there	are parts available.	☐
73	Children in films	have tutorial	arrangments so their	education continues.	☐
74	Filming can be	boring as hours	are waisted	awaiting your scene.	☐
75	The movie industry	is less glamorous	than it apears	in magazines.	☐

72 2

73 2

74 2

75 2

MARK ☐

COMPREHENSION SUB-TOTAL ☐ 30

Q. 76–85 Short writing task

MARK

Write for 20–30 minutes on *one* of the following. Continue on a separate sheet if you need to.

a) Continue the story 'My Big Day' from where it leaves off (page 16).

b) Imagine you are Mush. Tell the story from your point of view.

c) Think of a room you know well. Describe it in detail so that a reader can picture it clearly.

END OF TEST

SHORT WRITING TASK SUB-TOTAL		10
English skills sub-total (from page 15)		60
Comprehension sub-total (from page 18)		30
Short writing task sub-total (from this page)		10
PAPER 2 TOTAL MARK		100

Paper 3

START HERE

Q. 1–60 English skills

MARK

Q. 1–5
punctuation

Rewrite the text correctly, adding the necessary punctuation.

excuse me shouted asha can you help me im stuck up this tree and i cant get down

____

____

____

____

1–5 | 5

Q. 6–10
nouns

Add to the sentence a noun that is made from the word shown in capitals.

6 DECIDE It was a very tricky ______________ to make. — 6 | 1

7 PUNCTUAL Never late, he was well-known for his ______________. — 7 | 1

8 FAMOUS Mum's ______________ spread when her new DVD came out. — 8 | 1

9 REVEAL The newspaper's ______________ shocked us all. — 9 | 1

10 SPEAK I believe in the freedom of ______________ for all. — 10 | 1

Q. 11–15
word choice

Three words appear in brackets. Underline the *one* word that completes the sentence correctly.

11 A meteorite probably (destructed, destroyed, distracted) the dinosaurs. — 11 | 1

12 People who have seizures may suffer from (epilepsy, episodes, epicentre). — 12 | 1

13 The house was designed by a famous (archaeologist, artefact, architect). — 13 | 1

14 At university you can study many (disciplines, disciples, discussions). — 14 | 1

15 A naturalist studies the (habitats, inhabits, habitual) of different creatures. — 15 | 1

MARK

English skills

MARK

Q. 16–20 similes

Put the word in the simile to which it belongs.

houses, lamb, rock, rake, doornail

16 as dead as a ____________________ 16 [ ] 1

17 as thin as a ____________________ 17 [ ] 1

18 as steady as a ____________________ 18 [ ] 1

19 as safe as ____________________ 19 [ ] 1

20 as meek as a ____________________ 20 [ ] 1

Q. 21–25 parts of speech, verbs, adverbs

Read the sentence. Write V under the verb(s), P under the pronoun(s) and ADV under the adverb(s).

21 She pushed vigorously. 21 [ ] 1

22 They came here. 22 [ ] 1

23 We met before. 23 [ ] 1

24 He howled interminably. 24 [ ] 1

25 She ran doggedly round the track. 25 [ ] 1

Q. 26–30 abbreviations

Write the words that the abbreviation (shortened form) stands for.

26 NSPCC ____________________ 26 [ ] 1

27 UK ____________________ 27 [ ] 1

28 RAC ____________________ 28 [ ] 1

29 PO ____________________ 29 [ ] 1

30 MA ____________________ 30 [ ] 1

MARK [ ]

English skills

MARK

Q. 31–35 antonyms	Write down the antonym (opposite) of the word.	MARK
	31 professional ______________	31 1
	32 senior ______________	32 1
	33 elder ______________	33 1
	34 winning ______________	34 1
	35 remote ______________	35 1

Q. 36–40 word groups (by meaning)	Underline the *one* word that may be used to describe all the others.	MARK
	36 speak, communicate, write, telephone, text	36 1
	37 alder, cedar, birch, tree, beech	37 1
	38 fly, travel, sail, walk, ride	38 1
	39 spaniel, terrier, dog, Labrador, collie	39 1
	40 flu, measles, mumps, illness, chickenpox	40 1

Q. 41–45 apostrophes for possession	Abbreviate (shorten) the phrase by using an apostrophe. For example, *the bone belonging to the dog* becomes *the dog's bone.*	MARK
	41 the wings belonging to the fly ______________	41 1
	42 the uniform of the police officer ______________	42 1
	43 the house belonging to Mr Thomas ______________	43 1
	44 the tail of the lioness ______________	44 1
	45 the squeaks of the mice ______________	45 1

MARK

English skills

MARK

Q. 46–50
homonyms

Write the *one* word that has *both* meanings.

46 to get off (a bus, for example) / on fire ______________ 46 [ ] 1

47 form of transport with carriages / to teach someone a skill ______________ 47 [ ] 1

48 a postal label on a letter / to push down sharply with one's foot ______________ 48 [ ] 1

49 a herb / wise or a wise person ______________ 49 [ ] 1

50 to take something that is someone else's / to creep around quietly ______________ 50 [ ] 1

Q. 51–55
odd one out (by meaning)

Underline the *one* word that is the odd one out.

51 colleague, accomplice, helper, enemy, ally 51 [ ] 1

52 plumber, driver, bricklayer, electrician, plasterer 52 [ ] 1

53 lazy, mad, crazy, loony, nuts 53 [ ] 1

54 crab, plaice, halibut, bream, sardine 54 [ ] 1

55 academy, school, college, university, classroom 55 [ ] 1

Q. 56–60
spelling

Read the clue. Fill in the missing letters to make the word.

56 worried — a _ _ _ _ _ _ 56 [ ] 1

57 the opposite of ugly — b _ _ _ _ _ _ _ _ 57 [ ] 1

58 the flat surface above and facing the floor — c _ _ _ _ _ _ 58 [ ] 1

59 required, essential — n _ _ _ _ _ a _ _ 59 [ ] 1

60 a senior teacher at a university — p _ _ f _ _ _ _ _ 60 [ ] 1

MARK [ ]

ENGLISH SKILLS SUB-TOTAL [ ] 60

Q. 61–75 Comprehension

MARK

Read this passage carefully.

YOU CAN'T KEEP A GOOD MAN DOWN!

Stonecaster's mountain-climbing grandfather is off again.

A Stonecaster man is about to embark on a challenge. Pawel Robinski, 69, is packing his rucksack and ready to take on Mount Everest. He's no beginner, though he admits that Everest is quite daunting. He's a veteran of Kilimanjaro, 5 the highest mountain in Africa, followed by Aconcagua, the highest in the Americas, and Cho Oyu, another Himalayan monster. "I've been busy getting fit," says grandfather of three, Pawel. "Sean, the landlord of my local pub, The Three Pigeons, must wonder what's become of me as 10 I've been keeping off the beer. They see a lot more of me at the gym than the pub these days." However, he plans to pop into his local soon. "I hope they'll all sponsor me. All the regulars know me, so I'm sure they will."

However, preparations for the trip are hard work 15 and Pawel is looking forward to coming home again. "I'll be glad when it's done," he admits. "It's going to be an amazing adventure but all this abstinence is tough. I will be keen to get back to my real life – down The Pigeons and in my favourite Indian restaurant, the Koh-i-Noor on 20 Castle Street. I'll be pretty scrawny by the time I get back – and ready to put on a few pounds again!"

Pawel will raise money for the local hospice, Rosemead Priory. "Rosemead was great with my mum some years back, so I want to help them now that I can," says Pawel. 25 Elspeth Martin, Lead Consultant at Rosemead, says, "We're thrilled by Pawel's undertaking and we wish him all the best. Everyone at Rosemead is amazingly dedicated and selfless in their care for our residents and it is immensely rewarding when someone helps us in 30 this way in return."

Pawel plans to write a daily blog about his climb. "I want people back home – especially family and friends who sponsor me – to get a real feel for what it's like. I just hope my hands are not too cold to type!"

35 *If you would like to sponsor Pawel, visit www.pawelforeverest.com – where you can also see pictures of Pawel and his preparations for the trip.*

Now read these questions. You have a choice of four answers to each question. Choose the *one* answer you think the best. Draw a line in the box next to its letter, like this.

A ☐

61 The title of this article is 'You Can't Keep a Good Man Down!' In the context of the article as a whole, which word best describes this title?

A joke
B pun
C teaser
D heading

A ☐ B ☐ C ☐ D ☐

61 2

62 Pawel is ready 'to take on Mount Everest' (lines 2–3). What does the underlined phrase suggest about the peak?

A It is a very high mountain.
B It is a formidable enemy.
C It is waiting for Pawel.
D It is cold and dangerous.

A ☐ B ☐ C ☐ D ☐

62 2

MARK

Comprehension

MARK

63 Cho Oyu is described as 'another Himalayan monster' (lines 6–7). Which of the following phrases is closest to conveying this description of Cho Oyu?

A huge and dangerous
B savage and fierce
C ugly and predatory
D high up and frightening

A ☐ B ☐ C ☐ D ☐

63 ☐ 2

64 Who are 'the regulars' (line 13)?

A the people in the gym that Pawel uses
B the other mountain climbers
C the people that Pawel sees each day
D the people who often visit The Three Pigeons

A ☐ B ☐ C ☐ D ☐

64 ☐ 2

65 What is an experienced mountain climber known as?

A a mountainer
B a mounter
C a mountainous
D a mountaineer

A ☐ B ☐ C ☐ D ☐

65 ☐ 2

66 Pawel says that 'all this abstinence is tough' (line 17). What is 'abstinence'?

A giving up things you enjoy
B hard exercise and fitness training
C not drinking beer
D not eating Indian food

A ☐ B ☐ C ☐ D ☐

66 ☐ 2

67 Abstinence is a noun. Which *one* of the following is the related verb?

A abstine
B abstain
C abstone
D abstinate

A ☐ B ☐ C ☐ D ☐

67 ☐ 2

68 What is a 'hospice' (line 22)?

A a café where all are welcome
B an old people's home
C a nursing home that cares for people at the end of their lives
D a shop that sells things for charity

A ☐ B ☐ C ☐ D ☐

68 ☐ 2

MARK ☐

Comprehension

MARK

69 What is the meaning of 'dedicated and selfless' (line 28)?

A committed to working hard for others
B uncaring and selfish
C well-educated and energetic
D intelligent and careful

A ☐ B ☐ C ☐ D ☐

69 2

70 How does Pawel hope to share his adventure with others?

A by sending home photographs and getting people to sponsor him
B by drinking beer with his friends and writing a blog every day
C by sending home photographs and writing a blog every day
D by getting people to sponsor him and writing a blog every day

A ☐ B ☐ C ☐ D ☐

70 2

71 Which of the following phrases describes Pawel *least* accurately?

A adventurous and fit
B energetic and unselfish
C idle and uncaring
D brave and fearless

A ☐ B ☐ C ☐ D ☐

71 2

Find the grammatical mistake. Underline it and write the box letter at the end of the line.

	A	B	C	D	
72	Pawel, who's	very fit, is	considerably braver	than you or I.	☐
73	The mountain what	Pawel will climb	is apparently the	highest in the world.	☐
74	Me and my friend	raised money by	running 5 km	for the Hospice.	☐
75	We made more	for good causes	than we'd ever of	done otherwise.	☐

72 2

73 2

74 2

75 2

MARK

COMPREHENSION SUB-TOTAL 30

English
Progress Papers 1
Answers

Schofield&Sims

English Progress Papers 1

Notes for parents, tutors, teachers and other helpers

This pull-out book contains correct answers to all the questions in **English Progress Papers 1**, and is designed to assist you, the adult helper, as you mark the child's work. Once the child has become accustomed to the method of working, you may wish to give him or her direct access to this pull-out section.

When marking, write the number of marks achieved in the tinted column on the far right of the question page. The number to the right of the white mark box indicates the maximum mark available for that question. Sub-total boxes at the foot of each page will help you to add marks quickly. You can then fill in the total marks at the end of the paper. Here you can record separately the child's score in each of the three parts of the paper. The total score is out of 100 and therefore yields a percentage result. The child's progress can be recorded using the **Progress chart** on page 52.

Each paper is divided into three sections, as follows.

	Number of questions	**Total marks available**	**Approximate time available**
English skills	60	60	10–20 minutes
Comprehension	15	30	15–25 minutes
Short writing task	The child chooses and completes one of three tasks, for which 10 marks may be gained.	10	20–30 minutes
Totals	**85 questions**	**100 marks**	**45–75 minutes**

English skills (60 questions, worth a total of 60 marks)

This first section comprises 12 groups of five brief questions. In **English Progress Papers 1**, you can expect children to take between 10 and 20 minutes to complete it. Each group of questions tests a particular area of literacy skill or knowledge. Most of the questions in this first section have right or wrong answers (for example, the plural of *man* is *men*). However, some do not and a range of answers is possible. If the question asks, for example, for a sentence to be changed from indirect to direct speech then some variation from the suggested answer is acceptable. You must make your own judgement concerning these questions.

The questions in this section are worth one mark if answered correctly. The only exception is the somewhat longer punctuation question at the start of each paper, which is allocated a maximum of five marks. In all questions like these, where the right answer includes several different elements, give full marks only if the response is completely correct and covers all the constituent parts.

Some English words can be spelt correctly in more than one way. For a free download providing notes and guidance on alternative spellings, visit the Schofield & Sims website.

Comprehension (15 questions, worth a total of 30 marks)

The second section offers passages for comprehension followed by 15 multiple-choice questions, each with a choice of four possible answers – only one of which should be chosen. The Comprehension section in this book should take children between 15 and 25 minutes to answer. The questions vary in difficulty, but you should tell the child to assume that they are more difficult than they might at first appear. Encourage the child to read carefully both the passage and the question before answering. Sometimes, the distinction between several of the possible answers offered is subtle: care and re-reading of both the passage and the question may be needed before the choice is made.

A correctly answered Comprehension question is worth two marks. This reflects the importance of these questions, which test understanding of the passage as well as grammar and spelling.

Short writing task (worth a total of 10 marks)

The third section allows the child between 20 and 30 minutes to write a brief composition on one of three topics. Space is available for the piece of writing to be written on the page, directly below the list of topics. However, the child may need an extra sheet of paper on which to continue, so be sure to have some available.

Marking a child's composition is not an exact science, but generally speaking you should give credit for strengths and deduct marks for deficiencies. The guidelines below will help you to give the child's writing a mark out of 10. Please bear in mind that, at this level, it should not be impossible for a lively and accurately written piece to gain full marks.

Where an essay title is provided, this may be interpreted exactly as the child wishes. For example, the title 'Treasure!' (Paper 1, option b) could prompt the child to write a fictional story or a newspaper report. In total, this series provides 54 essay topics, requiring a range of writing skills and styles as listed opposite, used for a variety of purposes and aimed at different readers. Help the child to understand that not all writing is the same: they would not write a thank-you letter to their grandparents in the same style as a speech to be read out in class or a story for a younger child.

Give credit for:	**Deduct marks for:**
• writing in a style appropriate to the task and audience (see table opposite)	• inappropriate style – for example, too formal or informal for purpose and/or audience (see table opposite)
• correct spelling and punctuation, legible handwriting	• poor spelling and/or illegibility
• appropriate use of paragraphing and the setting out of dialogue	• inadequate or misplaced punctuation, paragraphing, use of capital letters
• correct grammar (allow some leeway for, for example, colloquial conversation, especially if it is expressive of individual character)	• writing that loses its way, is irrelevant to the title, doesn't make sense or is repetitive
• consistency within the piece of writing in the use of verb tenses	• inconsistent use of verb tenses – moving from past to present or vice versa
• use of interesting, varied and lively vocabulary	• inconsistent narrative approach – for example, changing from third person to first person or changing tenses mid-narrative
• narrative, descriptive or explicatory flair – for example, in holding the reader's attention, story twists, imaginative use of language	• a sense that the writer is not in control and is either struggling to write enough or struggling to contain an idea that is too big for the time allowed
• an overall sense of control and confidence	

The table opposite highlights different aspects of style – arranged by task type and designed to help you as you mark different types of writing. Discourage the child from always choosing the 'story' option. The experience of tackling the varied writing tasks provided in this series will give the child the skills and confidence to write well – not just in English tests but in all other aspects of study and life where writing matters.

Task type	Book 1
Story writing • A 30-minute time limit does not allow for a large cast or for several changes of place and day. The story will work best if the action happens all in one go, in one location and with only a few participants. • It is best for the child to avoid a long introduction, unless it is vital to the story. Award an extra mark if the child plunges straight into the story. This is particularly important, of course, if the child has been asked to continue the story where it left off or to write from a particular character's viewpoint. • Even bearing in mind these limitations, you may still find pace, dialogue and description that helps you to imagine the events, setting and atmosphere.	Paper 1b) Paper 4a) Paper 2a) Paper 5a) Paper 2b) Paper 6a) Paper 3a) Paper 6b)
Concise description • Look for evidence that the child has taken account of the intended audience for the piece of writing and adjusted his or her style accordingly. • For example, if the piece of writing requested is for a website or magazine, look for a concise style that will keep the attention of readers: watch out for too much detail, particularly any facts that are irrelevant to the audience.	Paper 1b) Paper 5a) Paper 3b) Paper 5c)
Detailed description • Where a full description is required, give marks for clearly imagined and carefully crafted prose. • Look for descriptions that give a strong sense of the person, place or thing.	Paper 1a) Paper 4a) Paper 1b) Paper 4c) Paper 2a) Paper 5b) Paper 2c) Paper 6b) Paper 3a) Paper 3c)
Instructions, persuasive writing and explanations • Clarity of thinking makes for clarity of expression. Before the child starts writing, he or she needs first to identify the purpose of the piece of writing. • *Instructions* need to be simple, correctly ordered and straightforward. • *Writing that aims to persuade or to influence* should avoid nagging or insulting the reader. Carefully worked-out arguments – clearly expressed and with separate points that are logically ordered – can be very effective. • *Explanation* must be clearly focused on exactly what it is that the reader needs to understand. Always look for evidence that the child understands what he or she is trying to explain. You cannot provide a clear explanation of something that you do not understand.	Paper 4b) Paper 5c)
Discussion • As above, look for clarity of thinking and expression, as well as evidence that the child has some understanding of the issue under discussion. • Strong opinions are not needed: being able to see several sides to a question is a valuable skill. • Simple sentences may work best in writing of this kind.	Paper 1c) Paper 6c)
Conversation and dialogue • Some questions invite the child to write a conversation, develop or create one or more characters, or speak in the voice of a particular character. Since we do not all speak in the same way, written conversation should convey a sense of the speaker, the context and the subject matter. • All conversation should be correctly set out and punctuated.	Paper 2b) Paper 5b) Paper 3b)

Paper 1
English skills

1–5 "Megan won't be at school in the morning because she'll be going to the dentist," Mrs Brown explained to the teacher.

6 height
7 receipt
8 marriage
9 ability
10 strength

11 who
12 Whom
13 their
14 lay
15 practise

16 famous
17 dangerous
18 exact
19 give
20 angry

There are several possible answers to questions 21–25. Those given are examples only.

21 "You have to re-do your homework," said the teacher. *or* "This homework has to be re-done," said the teacher. *or* "You must re-do your homework," said the teacher.
22 "Why are you so late getting home?" asked Mum. *or* "Why were you so late getting home?" asked Mum. *or* "What made you so late in getting home?" asked Mum.
23 "Harry, I'm really sorry about what I did," said George. *or* "Harry, I'm really sorry about what I have done," said George.

Paper 1 – *continued*

24 "I am sick of exams!" said the student. *or* "I am sick of taking exams!" said the student.
25 "Your laces are undone – again!" said my gran.

26 the men's shoes
27 our sisters-in-law
28 their mothers' birthdays
29 men, women and children
30 the dictionaries' definitions

31 It was the most interesting film we'd ever seen.
32 You'll probably miss your train if you don't hurry.
33 He'd grown so much I didn't recognise him.
34 Sanjay apologised so sincerely that he was let off.
35 Did you receive the present? I sent it first class.

36 European Union
37 world wide web
38 post scriptum *or* postscript
39 nota bene *(meaning 'note well')*
40 ante meridiem

41 colour (1), colt (2), cooler (3), cord (4), corridor (5)
42 dragging (1), dragon (2), dreary (3), drink (4), drip (5)
43 feel (1), felt (2), fence (3), ferry (4), fetch (5)
44 pheasant (1), philately (2), psalm (3), pseudo (4), psychiatrist (5)
45 ear (1), eerie (2), eerily (3), eeriness (4), eyrie (5)

46 permanent
47 departure
48 opaque
49 mean *or* miserly
50 contract *or* shrink

Paper 1 – *continued*

51 weaker, weakest
52 healthier, healthiest
53 more hopeful, most hopeful
54 smaller, smallest
55 kindlier/more kindly, kindliest/most kindly

56 one o'clock
57 he won't *or* he'll not
58 they don't
59 Isn't she going?
60 Where've you put my coat?

Comprehension

61 A
62 C
63 C
64 A
65 D
66 A
67 C
68 A
69 D
70 B
71 D
72 C sceintific *(should be 'scientific')*
73 C mythalogical *(should be 'mythological')*
74 B Whales *(should be 'Wales')*
75 C exept *(should be 'except')*

Short writing task

Refer to general guidelines on page A4 and specific notes on page A5 as indicated.

a) Detailed description
b) Story writing, Concise description, Detailed description
c) Discussion

Paper 2
English skills

1–5 "I'm very sorry, Dr Kumar isn't here at the moment," said the receptionist, "but he'll be back soon." *A comma or a dash may be used after the word 'sorry'.*

6 grandeur
7 success
8 curiosity
9 laziness
10 musician

11 shoot
12 minute
13 duck
14 spell
15 ginger

16 current
17 swam
18 principal
19 is *('are' would be an acceptable alternative in informal writing or in speech)*
20 prophesy

21 adjective
22 adverb
23 noun
24 verb
25 adjective

26 littler, littlest
27 worse, worst
28 more thoughtful, most thoughtful
29 tinier, tiniest
30 thinner, thinnest

31 crept
32 eaten
33 sung
34 fought
35 spoken

Paper 2 – *continued*

36 This is the <u>better</u> of the two games.
37 Each of the girls had <u>her</u> doll.
38 We <u>knew</u> she had <u>broken</u> her leg.
39 We couldn't answer <u>any</u> of the questions. *or* We <u>could</u> answer none of the questions.
40 Neither of them <u>was</u> hurt in the accident. *(In informal writing or in speech, 'Neither of them <u>were</u> hurt in the accident' would be acceptable.)*

41 Mum asked Kassim where he had been.
42 Tom said that he didn't feel very well.
43 Zofia replied that it was time she went to school.
44 Sam asked the attendant how far it was (*or* is) to Leeds. *or* Sam asked the attendant the distance to Leeds.
45 He replied that it was (*or* is) only about 10 miles.

46 accommodation
47 possess
48 occurrence
49 embarrass
50 immediately

51 happily
52 helpfully
53 casually
54 wisely
55 finely

56 You'll eat later.
57 Who's gone out?
58 I've had enough.
59 We can't find it.
60 All's well that ends well.

Paper 2 – *continued*
Comprehension

61 C
62 B
63 D
64 C
65 A
66 B
67 D
68 A
69 A
70 B
71 D
72 A usally *(should be 'usually')*
73 C arrangments *(should be 'arrangements')*
74 C waisted *(should be 'wasted')*
75 C apears *(should be 'appears')*

Short writing task

Refer to general guidelines on page A4 and specific notes on page A5 as indicated.

a) Story writing, Detailed description
b) Story writing, Conversation and dialogue
c) Detailed description

Paper 3
English skills

1–5 "Excuse me!" shouted Asha. "Can you help me? I'm stuck up this tree and I can't get down!" *A full stop could be used instead of the second exclamation mark – either would be correct.*

6 decision
7 punctuality
8 fame
9 revelation
10 speech

11 destroyed
12 epilepsy
13 architect
14 disciplines
15 habitats

16 doornail
17 rake
18 rock
19 houses
20 lamb

21 She (P) pushed (V) vigorously (ADV).
22 They (P) came (V) here (ADV).
23 We (P) met (V) before (ADV).
24 He (P) howled (V) interminably (ADV).
25 She (P) ran (V) doggedly (ADV) round the track.

26 National Society for the Prevention of Cruelty to Children
27 United Kingdom
28 Royal Automobile Club
29 Post Office
30 Master of Arts

Paper 3 – *continued*

31 amateur *or* lay *or* unprofessional
32 junior
33 younger
34 losing
35 close *or* near *or* central *Other possible antonyms include 'likely' or 'strong' (of a possibility) and 'friendly' or 'approachable' (of a person).*

36 communicate
37 tree
38 travel
39 dog
40 illness

41 the fly's wings
42 the police officer's uniform
43 Mr Thomas'(s) house
44 the lioness's tail
45 the mice's squeaks

46 alight
47 train
48 stamp
49 sage
50 steal

51 enemy
52 driver
53 lazy
54 crab
55 classroom

56 anxious
57 beautiful
58 ceiling
59 necessary
60 professor

Paper 3 – *continued*
Comprehension

61 B
62 B
63 A
64 D
65 D
66 A
67 B
68 C
69 A
70 D
71 C
72 D than you or I *(should be 'me')*
73 A The mountain what *(should be 'that')*
74 A Me and my friend *(should be 'My friend and I')*
75 C than we'd ever of *(should be 'have')*

Short writing task

Refer to general guidelines on page A4 and specific notes on page A5 as indicated.

a) Story writing, Detailed description
b) Concise description, Conversation and dialogue
c) Detailed description

Paper 4
English skills

1–5 "Help!" yelled the zoo keeper. "Cuthbert the lion has escaped!" *or* "Help!" yelled the zoo keeper, Cuthbert. "The lion has escaped!"

6 I can't wait until you get home – I must leave immediately.
7 Have you a piece of paper on which to write your address?
8 "Wait a minute!" he yelled. "I am buying some juice!"
9 Unusually, he didn't remember the beginning of the poem.
10 I'm completely exhausted and I need a chocolate biscuit!

11 plentiful *or* abundant *or* common
12 guilty
13 entrance *or* enter
14 difficult *or* hard
15 untidy *or* messy

16 He and I were playing outdoors.
17 The car passed me at great speed.
18 He has led me up the garden path.
19 Can I borrow your pen for a while?
20 He gave it to Louis and me.

21 type
22 stand
23 junk
24 fawn
25 spoke

Paper 4 – *continued*

26 lemonade
27 football
28 sandals
29 mansion
30 plumber

31 chosen
32 drunk
33 torn
34 ridden
35 laid

36 United Nations
37 post meridian
38 miles per hour
39 millimetre(s)
40 Her/His Royal Highness

41 I took the purse I had found to the police station. *or* I found a purse, which I took to the police station.
42 I went to see my gran, who lives in Hull.
43 He completed the walk, which was tiring.
44 She was late for school as (*or* because) she had got up late.
45 Bob catches the number 4 bus as (*or* because) it stops by his home. *or* Bob catches the number 4 bus, which stops by his home.

46 cheap/cheep
47 muscle/mussel
48 raw/roar
49 pause/paws
50 loan/lone

51 unique
52 infrequent
53 official
54 complement
55 rare

Paper 4 – *continued*

56 Liam's mum ate her son's (*or* sons') breakfast.
57 The boys did hours of work at their stepdad's farm.
58 The doctor's (*or* doctors') assistant came to the children's ward.
59 Mohammed's brother picked up the lady's cat.
60 The ladies' and gentlemen's toilets are at the back.

Comprehension

61 C
62 D
63 A
64 C
65 A
66 B
67 B
68 B
69 D
70 C
71 D
72 C puncuality *(should be 'punctuality')*
73 C especialy *(should be 'especially')*
74 B particulary *(should be 'particularly')*
75 D tunnells *(should be 'tunnels')*

Short writing task

Refer to general guidelines on page A4 and specific notes on page A5 as indicated.

a) Story writing, Detailed description
b) Instructions, persuasive writing and explanations
c) Detailed description

Paper 5
English skills

1–5 "Ow!" cried Annie's baby's nanny. "I think I've broken my ankle!"

6 depth
7 open
8 unfriendly *or* hostile
9 free *or* release
10 include

11 the butterfly's wings
12 the butterflies' wings
13 James'(s) football
14 three weeks' wages
15 half an hour's work

16 shoot (1), shore (2), short (3), shot (4), shrimp (5)
17 addict (1), ado (2), adore (3), adventure (4), advertise (5)
18 quarter (1), queasy (2), queueing (3), quirky (4), quite (5)
19 trip (1), tripe (2), triple (3), triplet (4), triplicate (5)
20 pool (1), pouch (2), poulterer (3), poultice (4), poultry (5)

21 luckier, luckiest
22 funnier, funniest
23 tastier, tastiest
24 heavier, heaviest
25 easier, easiest

26 length
27 width
28 height
29 depths
30 breadth

Paper 5 – *continued*

31 The contented cat (N) purred (V) as he lay (V) on the rug (N).
32 Enraged, Jacob (N) fought (V) off the attacker (N).
33 Mum (N) screamed (V) as the heavy book (N) fell (V) on her foot (N).
34 "Sit!"(V) shouted (V) Harry (N) to the excitable dog (N).
35 The fast hare (N) overtook (V) the slow tortoise (N).

36 want not
37 catches the worm
38 run deep
39 soonest mended
40 the sun shines

41 bank
42 room
43 tank
44 start
45 frank

46 justify
47 shelve
48 clothe
49 struck
50 horrified

51 mistook
52 misled
53 mislaid
54 misunderstood
55 miscast

56 cauliflower
57 elephant
58 pigeon
59 juggernaut
60 apostrophe

Paper 5 – *continued*
Comprehension

61 A
62 B
63 B
64 D
65 C
66 C
67 B
68 D
69 B
70 A
71 A
72 D felicities *(should be 'facilities')*
73 B conversationalists *(should be 'conservationists')*
74 B successively *(should be 'successfully')*
75 B respect *(should be 'aspect')*

Short writing task

Refer to general guidelines on page A4 and specific notes on page A5 as indicated.

a) Story writing, Concise description
b) Detailed description, Conversation and dialogue
c) Instructions, persuasive writing and explanations, Concise description

Paper 6
English skills

1–5 "My favourite book," said Lily, "is 'Horrid Henry' by Francesca Simon." *Ensure that the child uses capital letters for Horrid Henry, but omitting inverted commas around the title should not be treated as an error at this stage.*

6 The Captain ordered William to prepare to cast off.
7 Meena asked me whether I was (*or* am) going to take the test.
8 The plasterer told Dad to be careful as the floor was (*or* is) unsafe.
9 As Sam slunk in, the teacher told him that he was late again.
10 Oli asked if he might have some more as he was still hungry. *or* As Oli was still hungry, he asked if he might have some more.

11 counterfeit
12 sovereign
13 perceive
14 niece
15 weir

16 She didn't speak very clearly.
17 The teacher taught him many facts. *or* The teacher learned many facts. (*Omit 'him'.*)
18 She and I went shopping.
19 He was so helpful, I could have hugged him.
20 Priya laid the table before the meal.

Paper 6 – *continued*

21 eel
22 die
23 sheet
24 mustard
25 feather

26 inveigle
27 seize
28 heifer
29 receipt
30 sieve

31 lazy, lazily
32 thoughtful, thoughtfully
33 deep, deeply
34 high, highly
35 strong, strongly

36 Great Britain
37 kilometre(s)
38 United States of America
39 application (software)
40 Member of Parliament

41 I was so surprised at my success in the race.
42 I was jealous when he was made chief monitor.
43 I would definitely like to meet the author.
44 The builder was embarrassed when the ceiling fell in.
45 I will start my own business if I get the opportunity.

46 with a spine
47 awkward and difficult to handle
48 with both hands
49 survivor
50 eats meat

51 of
52 at *or* against
53 by
54 to
55 on

Paper 6 – *continued*

56 Spotting the burglar, Yossi raced after him.
57 Having picked up the bone, the dog (then) buried it.
58 Whistling my favourite song, I began vacuuming.
59 Finishing the race, he collapsed as he crossed the line.
60 Hanging on to the mugger, Chloë shouted for help. *or* Shouting for help, Chloë hung on to the mugger.

Comprehension

61 D
62 B
63 B
64 A
65 B
66 D
67 B
68 C
69 B
70 C
71 A
72 A likly *(should be 'likely')*
73 D descision *(should be 'decision')*
74 D payed *(should be 'paid')*
75 A actualy *(should be 'actually')*

Short writing task

Refer to general guidelines on page A4 and specific notes on page A5 as indicated.

a) Story writing
b) Story writing, Detailed description
c) Discussion

This book of answers is a pull-out section from
English Progress Papers 1

Published by **Schofield & Sims Ltd**,
7 Mariner Court, Wakefield, West Yorkshire WF4 3FL, UK
Telephone 01484 607080
www.schofieldandsims.co.uk

First published in 1993

Third impression 2019

Authors: **Patrick Berry and Susan Hamlyn**
Patrick Berry and Susan Hamlyn have asserted their moral rights under the Copyright, Designs and Patents Act, 1988, to be identified as the authors of this work.

British Library Cataloguing in Publication Data
A catalogue record for this book is available from the British Library.

Design by **Ledgard Jepson Ltd**

Printed in the UK by **Page Bros (Norwich) Ltd**

ISBN 978 07217 1473 8

Q. 76–85 Short writing task

MARK

Write for 20–30 minutes on *one* of the following. Continue on a separate sheet if you need to.

a) The Challenge

b) Write Pawel's blog the evening after he has spent a particularly difficult day on Everest.

c) You have never before seen snow and arrive for the first time in this country when everything is white. Write a letter home describing what you are experiencing.

END OF TEST

SHORT WRITING TASK SUB-TOTAL		10
English skills sub-total (from page 23)		60
Comprehension sub-total (from page 26)		30
Short writing task sub-total (from this page)		10
PAPER 3 TOTAL MARK		100

Paper 4

START HERE

Q. 1–60 English skills

MARK

Q. 1–5 punctuation

Rewrite the text correctly, adding the necessary punctuation.

help yelled the zoo keeper cuthbert the lion has escaped

____

____

____

1–5 ☐ 5

Q. 6–10 spelling

Write out the text, correcting any misspellings.

6 I can't wait untill you get home – I must leave immediatly.

____

____

6 ☐ 1

7 Have you a peice of paper on which to wright your adress?

____

____

7 ☐ 1

8 "Wait a minuit," he yelled. "I am buying some jiuce!"

____

____

8 ☐ 1

9 Unusally, he didn't rember the begining of the poem.

____

____

9 ☐ 1

10 I'm completly exorsted and I need a choclate biscit!

____

____

10 ☐ 1

Q. 11–15 antonyms

Write down the antonym (opposite) of the word.

11 scarce ______________ 11 ☐ 1

12 innocent ______________ 12 ☐ 1

13 exit ______________ 13 ☐ 1

14 easy ______________ 14 ☐ 1

15 neat ______________ 15 ☐ 1

MARK ☐

English skills

MARK

Q. 16–20
grammar, spelling

Write out the sentence, correcting any errors.

16 Him and me was playing outdoors.

______________________________ 16 [ ] 1

17 The car past me at great speed.

______________________________ 17 [ ] 1

18 He has lead me up the garden path.

______________________________ 18 [ ] 1

19 Can I lend your pen for a while?

______________________________ 19 [ ] 1

20 He gave it to Louis and I.

______________________________ 20 [ ] 1

Q. 21–25
homonyms

Write the *one* word that has *both* meanings.

21 a kind / used in printing ______________ 21 [ ] 1

22 a frame for displaying things / to be upright ______________ 22 [ ] 1

23 rubbish / a Chinese boat ______________ 23 [ ] 1

24 a young deer / to flatter in a slimy way ______________ 24 [ ] 1

25 talked / part of a bicycle wheel ______________ 25 [ ] 1

Q. 26–30
anagrams

Unscramble the anagram to fit the meaning given.
For example, *GENORA (a fruit)* is an *ORANGE*.

26 DELONAME (a drink) ______________ 26 [ ] 1

27 BOLTFOAL (a sport) ______________ 27 [ ] 1

28 DANLASS (footwear) ______________ 28 [ ] 1

29 NNMSAIO (a large house) ______________ 29 [ ] 1

30 BLUEPRM (someone who fixes leaks and drains) ______________ 30 [ ] 1

MARK [ ]

English skills

MARK

Q. 31–35
past tense

Add to the sentence the past tense of the verb shown in capitals.

31 CHOOSE I have ______________________ my new shoes. — 31 | 1

32 DRINK I have ______________________ too much. — 32 | 1

33 TEAR I have ______________________ my shirt. — 33 | 1

34 RIDE I have ______________________ Noah's bike. — 34 | 1

35 LAY He has ______________________ the table. — 35 | 1

Q. 36–40
abbreviations

Write the words that the abbreviation (shortened form) stands for.

36 UN ______________________ — 36 | 1

37 p.m. (as in 2.30 p.m.) ______________________ — 37 | 1

38 mph ______________________ — 38 | 1

39 mm ______________________ — 39 | 1

40 HRH ______________________ — 40 | 1

Q. 41–45
join sentences

Join the two sentences *without* using *and, but* or *so*.
For example, *The boy washed my car. I thanked the boy* becomes
I thanked the boy who washed my car or *I thanked the boy for washing my car.*

41 I found a purse. I took the purse to the police station.

______________________ — 41 | 1

42 I went to see my gran. My gran lives in Hull.

______________________ — 42 | 1

43 He completed the walk. The walk was tiring.

______________________ — 43 | 1

44 She was late for school. She had got up late.

______________________ — 44 | 1

45 Bob catches the number 4 bus. It stops by his home.

____

______________________ — 45 | 1

MARK

English skills

MARK

Q. 46–50
homophones

Read the clues, then write the homophones (words that sound the same).
For example, *water from above* is rain / *what the monarch does* is reign.

46 inexpensive ____________ / a chirp made by a young bird ____________ 46 [ ] 1

47 part of the body that helps us move ____________ / a shellfish ____________ 47 [ ] 1

48 uncooked ____________ / a lion does it ____________ 48 [ ] 1

49 a short break ____________ / animal feet ____________ 49 [ ] 1

50 borrowed money ____________ / solitary ____________ 50 [ ] 1

Q. 51–55
word choice

Put the word in the sentence where it makes the best sense.

official, complement, unique, rare, infrequent

51 This vase is ________________________, being the only one of its kind. 51 [ ] 1

52 The village receives only an ________________________ bus service. 52 [ ] 1

53 It's an ________________________ sign so we'd better not trespass. 53 [ ] 1

54 The mustard was the perfect ________________________ to the steak. 54 [ ] 1

55 The eggs of ________________________ birds are protected by law. 55 [ ] 1

Q. 56–60
apostrophes for possession

Rewrite the sentence, adding apostrophe(s) as you do so.

56 Liams mum ate her sons breakfast.

____ 56 [ ] 1

57 The boys did hours of work at their stepdads farm.

____ 57 [ ] 1

58 The doctors assistant came to the childrens ward.

____ 58 [ ] 1

59 Mohammeds brother picked up the ladys cat.

____ 59 [ ] 1

60 The ladies and gentlemens toilets are at the back.

____ 60 [ ] 1

MARK [ ]

ENGLISH SKILLS SUB-TOTAL [ ] 60

Q. 61–75 Comprehension

MARK

Read this passage carefully.

No Time to Lose

Cassie is worried about her grandfather.

The inhaler was lying there on the table. Cassie froze.

"Oh no!" she breathed. "Not again!"

She looked at the little green clock on the cooker. 12.17. The train was due to leave at 12.34 and he'd been gone around four minutes. Could she – if she ran like a racehorse – get to the station before he got
5 on the train? She grabbed her jacket, her keys and her purse. The laces of her trainers were undone and her fingers struggled to tie them, too fast to be accurate. She tore open the front door and slammed it behind her, already half way down the path as it banged shut.

Her brain raced. Which was the quickest way? Was it best to guess which route he'd have taken and try to head him off? Was it better to just get to the station the fastest possible way and hope to be there
10 when he arrived? But there were two entrances to the station. He might take either. What should she do?

She pictured him, as she pelted through the shopping centre, sitting on the train, the train slipping away from the platform and then, suddenly, his breath going, his throat constricting, his face turning beige as the air wouldn't come, choking, collapsing . . . He'd fumble for the inhaler – the other passengers wouldn't understand, they'd think he was drunk, they'd ignore him – and the inhaler wouldn't be
15 in his pocket.

A woman was setting out a table in front of her café. Two men came out, laughing. There was no space between them and the table. Cassie couldn't avoid them. She hurtled into them, sending one staggering into the wall.

"Sorry!" she tried to call out as she shot between them, but she had no breath left to make a sound.
20 The shopping centre clock clanged 12.30 and she still hadn't seen her grandfather.

Now read these questions. You have a choice of four answers to each question. Choose the *one* answer you think the best. Draw a line in the box next to its letter, like this.

A ☐

61 What illness might someone who uses an inhaler (line 1) suffer from?

A eczema
B catarrh
C asthma
D arthritis

A ☐ B ☐ C ☐ D ☐

61 2

62 How long did Grandfather have between his leaving the house and the departure of the train?

A 19 minutes
B 27 minutes
C 13 minutes
D 21 minutes

A ☐ B ☐ C ☐ D ☐

62 2

MARK

Comprehension

MARK

63 'if she ran like a racehorse' (line 4) is an example of a literary device. What is it called?

A a simile
B a personification
C an exaggeration
D an adjective

A ☐ B ☐ C ☐ D ☐

63 ☐ 2

64 Which of the words below would best complete the sentence?

Cassie evidently feels a great sense of ______________ towards her grandfather.

A antipathy
B impatience
C responsibility
D pity

A ☐ B ☐ C ☐ D ☐

64 ☐ 2

65 Which of the following proverbs is suggested by Cassie's problems with her laces?

A More haste, less speed.
B Look before you leap.
C Many hands make light work.
D A miss is as good as a mile.

A ☐ B ☐ C ☐ D ☐

65 ☐ 2

66 'She tore open the front door and slammed it behind her, already half way down the path as it banged shut' (lines 6–7). How many verbs are there in this sentence?

A four
B three
C one
D two

A ☐ B ☐ C ☐ D ☐

66 ☐ 2

67 Cassie is uncertain about what to do (lines 8–10). Which of the following words best sums up her state of mind in these lines?

A confusion
B dilemma
C panic
D hysteria

A ☐ B ☐ C ☐ D ☐

67 ☐ 2

68 Cassie imagines her grandfather having an attack (lines 11–15). Which *one* of the following is *not* worrying her?

A he will become seriously ill on the train
B he won't have enough money
C he has left his inhaler at home
D the other passengers won't understand what is wrong with him

A ☐ B ☐ C ☐ D ☐

68 ☐ 2

MARK ☐

Comprehension

MARK

69 Cassie 'hurtled' into the men (line 17). Which of the following words is similar in meaning to 'hurtled'?

A fell
B smacked
C sped
D careered

A ☐ B ☐ C ☐ D ☐

69 ☐ 2

70 Later in the story, Cassie reaches her grandfather just in time. If you were him, which *two* of the following words would describe your feelings?

1. grateful 2. apologetic 3. unconcerned 4. irritated

A 3 and 4 only
B 2 and 3 only
C 1 and 2 only
D 1 and 3 only

A ☐ B ☐ C ☐ D ☐

70 ☐ 2

71 Which of the following is the best alternative title for this passage?

A Station Drama
B Granddad Forgets
C Old and Young
D Race Against Time

A ☐ B ☐ C ☐ D ☐

71 ☐ 2

Find the spelling mistake. Underline it and write the box letter at the end of the line.

72

A	B	C	D	
Passengers are	more irritated by	lack of puncuality	than by dirty carriages.	☐

72 ☐ 2

73

A	B	C	D	
Asthma is an	unpleasant condition,	especialy for children	and the elderly.	☐

73 ☐ 2

74

A	B	C	D	
Many children	have particulary	affectionate relationships	with grandparents.	☐

74 ☐ 2

75

A	B	C	D	
Sensations of	claustrophobia may	occur when travelling	through tunnells.	☐

75 ☐ 2

MARK ☐

COMPREHENSION SUB-TOTAL ☐ 30

Q. 76–85 Short writing task

MARK

Write for 20–30 minutes on *one* of the following. Continue on a separate sheet if you need to.

a) Continue the story 'No Time to Lose' from where it leaves off (page 32).

b) Think of a gadget, game or tool you know well. Write careful instructions for its use.

c) Think of an elderly person you know well. Describe them, conveying an impression of their appearance and personality.

END OF TEST

SHORT WRITING TASK SUB-TOTAL		10
English skills sub-total (from page 31)		60
Comprehension sub-total (from page 34)		30
Short writing task sub-total (from this page)		10
PAPER 4 TOTAL MARK		100

Paper 5

START HERE

Q. 1–60 English skills

MARK

Q. 1–5 punctuation

Rewrite the text correctly, adding the necessary punctuation.

ow cried annies babys nanny i think ive broken my ankle

______

______

______

1–5 [ ] 5

Q. 6–10 antonyms

Write down the antonym (opposite) of the word.

			Mark
6	height	______	6 [ ] 1
7	closed	______	7 [ ] 1
8	friendly	______	8 [ ] 1
9	imprison	______	9 [ ] 1
10	exclude	______	10 [ ] 1

Q. 11–15 apostrophes for possession

Rewrite the phrase, adding an apostrophe as you do so.

			Mark
11	the butterflys wings	______	11 [ ] 1
12	the butterflies wings	______	12 [ ] 1
13	James football	______	13 [ ] 1
14	three weeks wages	______	14 [ ] 1
15	half an hours work	______	15 [ ] 1

MARK [ ]

English skills

MARK

Q. 16–20 alphabetical order

Put the words in alphabetical order by writing the numbers from 1 to 5 in the brackets.

16 shoot (___), short (___), shore (___), shot (___), shrimp (___) — 16 [ ] 1

17 adventure (___), advertise (___), adore (___), addict (___), ado (___) — 17 [ ] 1

18 queueing (___), quirky (___), queasy (___), quarter (___), quite (___) — 18 [ ] 1

19 triplet (___), triple (___), triplicate (___), trip (___), tripe (___) — 19 [ ] 1

20 poultry (___), pouch (___), poulterer (___), poultice (___), pool (___) — 20 [ ] 1

Q. 21–25 comparative and superlative

Using the example as a guide, write the comparative and superlative of the adjective given.

	ADJECTIVE	COMPARATIVE	SUPERLATIVE	
Example:	DIRTY	*dirtier*	*dirtiest*	
21	LUCKY	________	________	21 [ ] 1
22	FUNNY	________	________	22 [ ] 1
23	TASTY	________	________	23 [ ] 1
24	HEAVY	________	________	24 [ ] 1
25	EASY	________	________	25 [ ] 1

Q. 26–30 nouns

Add to the sentence a noun that is made from the word shown in capitals.

26 LONG The swimming pool's __________ is enough for Olympic training. — 26 [ ] 1

27 WIDE Can you work out the __________ of the garden? — 27 [ ] 1

28 HIGH The __________ of some city buildings is breathtaking! — 28 [ ] 1

29 DEEP Some creatures live at enormous __________ at the bottom of the ocean. — 29 [ ] 1

30 BROAD I measured the __________ of the canvas to make my tent. — 30 [ ] 1

MARK [ ]

English skills

MARK

Q. 31–35
parts of speech, nouns, verbs

Read the sentence. Write N under the noun(s) and V under the verb(s).

31 The contented cat purred as he lay on the rug. — 31 [ ] 1

32 Enraged, Jacob fought off the attacker. — 32 [ ] 1

33 Mum screamed as the heavy book fell on her foot. — 33 [ ] 1

34 "Sit!" shouted Harry to the excitable dog. — 34 [ ] 1

35 The fast hare overtook the slow tortoise. — 35 [ ] 1

Q. 36–40
proverbs and sayings

Complete the proverb or saying.

36 Waste not, ______________________. — 36 [ ] 1

37 The early bird ______________________. — 37 [ ] 1

38 Still waters ______________________. — 38 [ ] 1

39 Least said, ______________________. — 39 [ ] 1

40 Make hay while ______________________. — 40 [ ] 1

Q. 41–45
homonyms

Write the *one* word that has *both* meanings.

41 at the edge of a river / place to keep money ______________ — 41 [ ] 1

42 space / one of several within a house or flat ______________ — 42 [ ] 1

43 place for fuel in a car / armoured vehicle ______________ — 43 [ ] 1

44 to begin / to jump with surprise ______________ — 44 [ ] 1

45 outspoken, honest / to stamp with an official mark ______________ — 45 [ ] 1

MARK [ ]

English skills

MARK

Q. 46–50
verbs

Add to the sentence a verb that is made from the word shown in capitals.

46 JUST I hope he can ________________ what he has done. 46 [ ] 1

47 SHELF We must ________________ our plans until later. 47 [ ] 1

48 CLOTH I need money to feed and ________________ the baby. 48 [ ] 1

49 STRIKE We ________________ up an agreement. 49 [ ] 1

50 HORROR He ________________ me by telling me the cost. 50 [ ] 1

Q. 51–55
past tense

Add to the sentence the past tense of the verb shown in capitals.

51 MISTAKE He ________________ me for someone else. 51 [ ] 1

52 MISLEAD When he told me the way he ________________ me. 52 [ ] 1

53 MISLAY She has ________________ her racquet and cannot play. 53 [ ] 1

54 MISUNDERSTAND The child had ________________ all we'd said. 54 [ ] 1

55 MISCAST The actor playing The Doctor was ________________ in that role. 55 [ ] 1

Q. 56–60
anagrams

Unscramble the anagram to fit the meaning given.
For example, *A DIRTY COIN (a book for checking spelling)* is a *DICTIONARY*.

56 COW I ARE FULL (a vegetable) ________________ 56 [ ] 1

57 NEAT HELP (an animal) ________________ 57 [ ] 1

58 ONE PIG (a bird) ________________ 58 [ ] 1

59 RUN JUG GATE (a large vehicle) ________________ 59 [ ] 1

60 PAT SHE POOR (a punctuation mark) ________________ 60 [ ] 1

MARK [ ]

ENGLISH SKILLS SUB-TOTAL [ ] 60

Q. 61–75 Comprehension

MARK

Read this passage carefully.

VISIT THE BIRDERIE

. . . and spread your wings!

The Birderie is Grainshire's most exciting family resort. Set in 25 acres of English countryside, The Birderie is home to hundreds of birds – the beautiful, the exotic, the shy, the sociable, the fierce, the friendly and the just plain weird!

5 Get eyeball to eyeball with diving penguins in our Underwater Walk. Trail through the treetops on our Bird's Eye View tour and watch the hawks catch their prey mid-flight in our Falconry Fiesta. Sneak a peek at the shamelessly flirtatious lovebirds in our African Aviary and munch 10 your lunch with our chatty mynah birds.

Visit Haystack Farm and witness chicks hatching out of their shells. Meet Chanticleer the famous cockerel and his many wives. Paddle your own canoe around Donald's Duckpond and watch feeding time for our fabulous 15 flamingos and crowned cranes on the Tropical Lake.

The Birderie is home to exciting birds from all over the world, but it has a serious side too. Avian Hospital cares for sick and injured birds brought in from all over the UK. Our scientists and conservationists carry out essential work 20 in learning how to preserve endangered species, safeguard threatened habitats, monitor our own bird population and analyse the effects of invasive species, farming practices and diminishing nesting areas. You can see our experts at work and watch, in our comfortable cinema, the fascinating 25 and moving film 'Flying to Live'.

Why not take part in our Bird Identity Parade and learn how to identify the birds around us? You'll be amazed to learn how many birds you can see in your own neighbourhood. Find out how you can contribute to looking 30 after the birds in your own garden or local park.

Come out of your shell and spread your wings! Visit The Birderie for a cracking day out!

Now read these questions. You have a choice of four answers to each question. Choose the *one* answer you think the best. Draw a line in the box next to its letter, like this.

A ☐

61 How many adjectives can you find in paragraph 1?

A nine
B seven
C five
D ten

A ☐ B ☐ C ☐ D ☐

61 ☐ 2

62 An 'acre', line 2, is a measurement of space. Three of the words listed below are also measurements of space or distance. Which one is *not*?

A hectare
B knot
C square mile
D league

A ☐ B ☐ C ☐ D ☐

62 ☐ 2

63 The first paragraph explains that there are many different birds in The Birderie. Which of the words below would best complete the sentence?

The collection of birds in The Birderie is remarkable for its ________________.

A colour
B diversity
C strangeness
D behaviour

A ☐ B ☐ C ☐ D ☐

63 ☐ 2

MARK ☐

Comprehension

MARK

64 What is the main point of the second paragraph?

A to describe the variety of things that visitors can do at the Birderie
B to show the cleverness of the birds
C to list the different levels of bird life at the Birderie
D to let visitors know how closely they can get involved with the birds

A ☐ B ☐ C ☐ D ☐

64 ☐ 2

65 The phrases 'Underwater Walk', 'trail through the treetops', 'Falconry Fiesta', 'sneak a peek', 'African Aviary' and 'munch your lunch' appear in the second paragraph. Which *two* of the following best describe the writing techniques used?

1. rhyme 2. imagination 3. description 4. alliteration

A 2 and 3
B 2 and 1
C 4 and 1
D 4 and 3

A ☐ B ☐ C ☐ D ☐

65 ☐ 2

66 A 'Tropical Lake' is mentioned (line 15). Where would you normally find tropical places?

A north of the equator
B south of the equator
C north and south of the equator
D on the equator

A ☐ B ☐ C ☐ D ☐

66 ☐ 2

67 The words 'aviary' (line 9) and 'avian' (line 17) are derived from the Latin for the word 'bird', which is 'avis'. Which of the following has the same derivation?

A avoid
B aviator
C avocado
D avid

A ☐ B ☐ C ☐ D ☐

67 ☐ 2

68 Line 21 refers to 'threatened habitats'. Which of the following phrases means the same thing?

A frightening behaviour
B strange customs
C damaged homes
D endangered living areas

A ☐ B ☐ C ☐ D ☐

68 ☐ 2

MARK ☐

Comprehension

MARK

69 Which of the words below would best complete the sentence?

Some of our species of birds are finding it hard to survive because areas of land in which they can nest are ______________.

A invasive
B shrinking
C flooded
D dangerous

A ☐ B ☐ C ☐ D ☐

69 2

70 What is the name that we give to a scientific expert on the subject of birds?

A an ornithologist
B an aviatrix
C a birdiologist
D a biologist

A ☐ B ☐ C ☐ D ☐

70 2

71 What is the principal purpose of this article?

A to persuade people to visit The Birderie
B to educate people about birds
C to let people know what happens at The Birderie
D to explain the many different things birds do

A ☐ B ☐ C ☐ D ☐

71 2

Find the word that is used wrongly. Underline it and write the box letter at the end of the line.

72 Theme parks are (A) under pressure to (B) provide more (C) felicities for visitors. (D) ☐

72 2

73 Zoos employ (A) conversationalists to (B) study the health (C) of their inhabitants. (D) ☐

73 2

74 Some species only (A) breed successively if (B) carefully nurtured (C) in captivity. (D) ☐

74 2

75 One extraordinary (A) respect of birds is (B) their diversity in (C) appearance and size. (D) ☐

75 2

MARK ☐

COMPREHENSION SUB-TOTAL ☐ 30

Q. 76–85 Short writing task

MARK

Write for 20–30 minutes on *one* of the following. Continue on a separate sheet if you need to.

a) The Visit

b) You are a bird perched on top of a tree near your home. Describe the scene in detail from your point of view.

c) Think of a theme park, animal centre, museum or other place to visit that you know well. Write a leaflet to advertise its attractions to potential visitors.

END OF TEST

SHORT WRITING TASK SUB-TOTAL		10
English skills sub-total (from page 39)		60
Comprehension sub-total (from page 42)		30
Short writing task sub-total (from this page)		10
PAPER 5 TOTAL MARK		100

Paper 6

START HERE

Q. 1–60 English skills

MARK

Q. 1–5 punctuation

Rewrite the sentence correctly, adding the necessary punctuation.

my favourite book said lily is horrid henry by francesca simon

____

____

____

1–5 ☐ 5

Q. 6–10 direct to indirect speech

Change the text from direct to indirect (reported) speech.

6 "Prepare to cast off!" the Captain ordered William.

____ 6 ☐ 1

7 "Are you going to take the test?" asked Meena.

____ 7 ☐ 1

8 "Be careful," said the plasterer to Dad, "the floor is unsafe."

____

____ 8 ☐ 1

9 "You're late again," the teacher told Sam as he slunk in.

____

____ 9 ☐ 1

10 "May I have some more?" asked Oli. "I'm still hungry."

____

____ 10 ☐ 1

Q. 11–15 spelling

Fill in **ie** or **ei** to make the word.

11 counterf ___ ___ t — 11 ☐ 1

12 sover ___ ___ gn — 12 ☐ 1

13 perc ___ ___ ve — 13 ☐ 1

14 n ___ ___ ce — 14 ☐ 1

15 w ___ ___ r — 15 ☐ 1

MARK ☐

English skills

MARK

Q. 16–20 grammar

Write out the sentence, correcting any errors.

16 She didn't speak very clear.

______________________________ 16 [ ] 1

17 The teacher learned him many facts.

______________________________ 17 [ ] 1

18 Me and her went shopping.

______________________________ 18 [ ] 1

19 He was so helpful, I could of hugged him.

______________________________ 19 [ ] 1

20 Priya lay the table before the meal.

______________________________ 20 [ ] 1

Q. 21–25 similes

Put the word in the simile to which it belongs.

feather, sheet, mustard, die, eel

21 as slippery as an ________________ 21 [ ] 1

22 as straight as a ________________ 22 [ ] 1

23 as white as a ________________ 23 [ ] 1

24 as keen as ________________ 24 [ ] 1

25 as light as a ________________ 25 [ ] 1

Q. 26–30 spelling

Fill in **ie** or **ei** to make the word.

26 inv ___ ___ gle 26 [ ] 1

27 s ___ ___ ze 27 [ ] 1

28 h ___ ___ fer 28 [ ] 1

29 rec ___ ___ pt 29 [ ] 1

30 s ___ ___ ve 30 [ ] 1

MARK [ ]

English skills

MARK

Q. 31–35

parts of speech, nouns, adjectives, adverbs

Write the missing parts of speech of the words shown in capitals.

	NOUN	ADJECTIVE	ADVERB	
Example:	BRAVERY	*brave*	*bravely*	
31	LAZINESS	______	______	31 1
32	THOUGHT	______	______	32 1
33	DEPTH	______	______	33 1
34	HEIGHT	______	______	34 1
35	STRENGTH	______	______	35 1

Q. 36–40

abbreviations

Write the words that the abbreviation (shortened form) stands for.

36 GB ______ 36 1

37 km ______ 37 1

38 USA ______ 38 1

39 app ______ 39 1

40 MP ______ 40 1

Q. 41–45

spelling

Write out the sentence, correcting any misspellings.

41 I was so suprised at my succes in the race.

______ 41 1

42 I was jelous when he was made cheif monitor.

______ 42 1

43 I would definately like to meet the auther.

______ 43 1

44 The bilder was embarased when the cieling fell in.

______ 44 1

45 I will start my own bisness if I get the oportunity.

______ 45 1

MARK

English skills

MARK

Q. 46–50
word meanings

Three words or phrases appear in brackets. Underline the *one* word or phrase that completes the sentence correctly.

46 A vertebrate is a creature . . .
(with a spine, with a thick skin, able to swim and walk).

46 ☐ 1

47 Something cumbersome is . . .
(loud and noisy, awkward and difficult to handle, cuddly and soft).

47 ☐ 1

48 An ambidextrous person can do things . . .
(with both hands, with their eyes shut, incredibly fast).

48 ☐ 1

49 Someone who gets out alive from a disaster is a . . .
(successor, submariner, survivor).

49 ☐ 1

50 A carnivore is a person or animal who . . .
(enjoys parties, is good at games, eats meat).

50 ☐ 1

Q. 51–55
prepositions

Add the correct preposition to complete the sentence.

51 He despaired ____________________ ever finding a job. — 51 ☐ 1

52 We protested ____________________ the army's use of force. — 52 ☐ 1

53 She was inspired ____________________ his teaching. — 53 ☐ 1

54 According ____________________ the website, the game is cancelled. — 54 ☐ 1

55 Can you comment ____________________ what you saw? — 55 ☐ 1

Q. 56–60
join sentences

Join the two sentences *without* using *and, but* or *so*. Begin each new sentence with a word ending in *ing* and use a comma.
For example, *Ian left his warm bed. He shivered as he put on his slippers* becomes *Leaving his warm bed, Ian shivered as he put on his slippers.*

56 Yossi spotted the burglar. Yossi raced after him.

____

56 ☐ 1

57 The dog picked up the bone. He buried it.

____

57 ☐ 1

58 I whistled my favourite song. I began vacuuming.

____

58 ☐ 1

59 He finished the race. He collapsed as he crossed the line.

____

____

59 ☐ 1

60 Chloë hung on to the mugger. She shouted for help.

____

60 ☐ 1

MARK ☐

ENGLISH SKILLS SUB-TOTAL ☐ 60

Q. 61–75 Comprehension

MARK

Read this passage carefully.

Holiday Heartbreak

Laura and Rupa find themselves in a difficult situation.

"It's only two weeks till we go!" enthused Laura.
"Oh, yeah. Hm!"
"I just can't wait to show you the White Water Rapids – it's just the most amazing fun in the whole resort!"
5 "I bet. Yeah! It must be."
"It's just brilliant that Mum and Dad said you could come. It'll be *so* much better than being on my own with Toby and Rajiv. They are *so* boring and they just want to play snooker the whole day."
"Er . . ." Rupa hesitated. "It *is* incredible that your mum and dad invited me. It was so kind of them. It's even more amazing that my parents said I could go . . . but . . ."
10 "Yeah! I didn't think they would either. I mean, they didn't even want you to come bowling when we went for Yasmin's party, did they?"
"No – well, they are a bit insane about homework, you know."
"I hope we're in the Lakeside Cabin – it's simply the best. You can watch herons flapping over the lake while you have breakfast. They have the most ginormous wings!"
15 "Hm! Sounds good. Er . . ."
"Er *what*? You're not sounding all that excited any more. You haven't gone off the idea?"
"Er . . ."
"Roops! What is it? What's happened?"
"Well, nothing exactly happened . . ."
20 "Well, then, *what*? You're my bestest friend!"
"I know! And you're mine! It's just . . ."
"*WHAT?*"
Rupa paused. She drew a deep breath.
"Imran's coming from America. He gets in the day we're supposed to be going away. He leaves the day
25 we get back. If I come away with you, I will miss him. *Completely!*"
Laura went very pale.
"Oh no. And I will miss him too!"
The girls stood still, in silence, both of them heartbroken, thinking of Rupa's film-star cousin and how, over all the years of their friendship, they had dreamed of meeting him.

Now read these questions. You have a choice of four answers to each question. Choose the *one* answer you think the best. Draw a line in the box next to its letter, like this.

A [—]

61 How many people are booked to go on the holiday?

A five
B four
C eight
D six

A ☐ B ☐ C ☐ D ☐

61 ☐ 2

MARK ☐

Comprehension

MARK

62 Laura refers to the 'White Water Rapids' (line 3). What activity do you think takes place here?

A floating
B rafting
C rowing
D sailing

A ☐ B ☐ C ☐ D ☐ — 62 / 2

63 Rupa hesitates in line 8. Why?

A because she does not now want to go on the holiday
B because she has something to tell Laura and doesn't know how
C because she is worried about her parents
D because she doesn't want to be rude to Laura's parents

A ☐ B ☐ C ☐ D ☐ — 63 / 2

64 Which of the words below would best complete the sentence?

Rupa's parents are clearly very ________________ about homework.

A demanding
B reasonable
C mad
D persistent

A ☐ B ☐ C ☐ D ☐ — 64 / 2

65 Laura enthuses about the 'most ginormous wings' of the herons (line 14). Which of the words below means 'to make something bigger'?

A expend
B expand
C export
D express

A ☐ B ☐ C ☐ D ☐ — 65 / 2

66 Which of the words below would best complete the sentence?

Rupa's revelation is likely to put a considerable strain on their ________________.

A holiday
B conversation
C parents
D friendship

A ☐ B ☐ C ☐ D ☐ — 66 / 2

67 Which of the words below would best complete the sentence?

Unfortunately, Imran's visit exactly ________________ with the holiday.

A concludes
B coincides
C coexists
D combines

A ☐ B ☐ C ☐ D ☐ — 67 / 2

MARK ☐

Comprehension

MARK

68 Which of the words below would best complete the sentence?

The girls feel that to miss Imran's visit would be ______________.

A incomparable
B imperceivable
C unimaginable
D unintentional

A ☐ B ☐ C ☐ D ☐

68 2

69 Why is '*Completely!*' (line 25) shown in italics?

A because it is a word on its own
B for emphasis
C because it has an exclamation mark
D because Rupa is upset

A ☐ B ☐ C ☐ D ☐

69 2

70 Identify the types of words contained in the phrase 'The girls stood still, in silence' (line 28).

A two nouns, one verb and an adjective
B one noun, one verb and an adjective
C two nouns, one verb and an adverb
D one noun, one verb and an adverb

A ☐ B ☐ C ☐ D ☐

70 2

71 Which term best describes the passage?

A dialogue
B monologue
C playscript
D discussion

A ☐ B ☐ C ☐ D ☐

71 2

Find the spelling mistake. Underline it and write the box letter at the end of the line.

72 Laura is likly to be | disappointed by | Rupa's news a | fortnight before their trip.

A	B	C	D	☐

72 2

73 Rupa is having a | crisis of conscience | and has a difficult | descision to make.

A	B	C	D	☐

73 2

74 Rupa's parents are | embarrassed as | Laura's parents have | payed a deposit

A	B	C	D	☐

74 2

75 What actualy happens is that Imran can't come because of filming commitments.

A	B	C	D	☐

75 2

MARK ☐

COMPREHENSION SUB-TOTAL ☐ 30

Q. 76–85 Short writing task

MARK

Write for 20–30 minutes on *one* of the following. Continue on a separate sheet if you need to.

a) Continue the story 'Holiday Heartbreak' from where it leaves off (page 48).

b) The Event

c) What makes a good friend?

END OF TEST

SHORT WRITING TASK SUB-TOTAL		10
English skills sub-total (from page 47)		60
Comprehension sub-total (from page 50)		30
Short writing task sub-total (from this page)		10
PAPER 6 TOTAL MARK		100

Progress chart

Write the score (out of 100) for each paper in the box provided at the bottom of the chart.
Then colour in the column above the box to the appropriate height to represent this score.

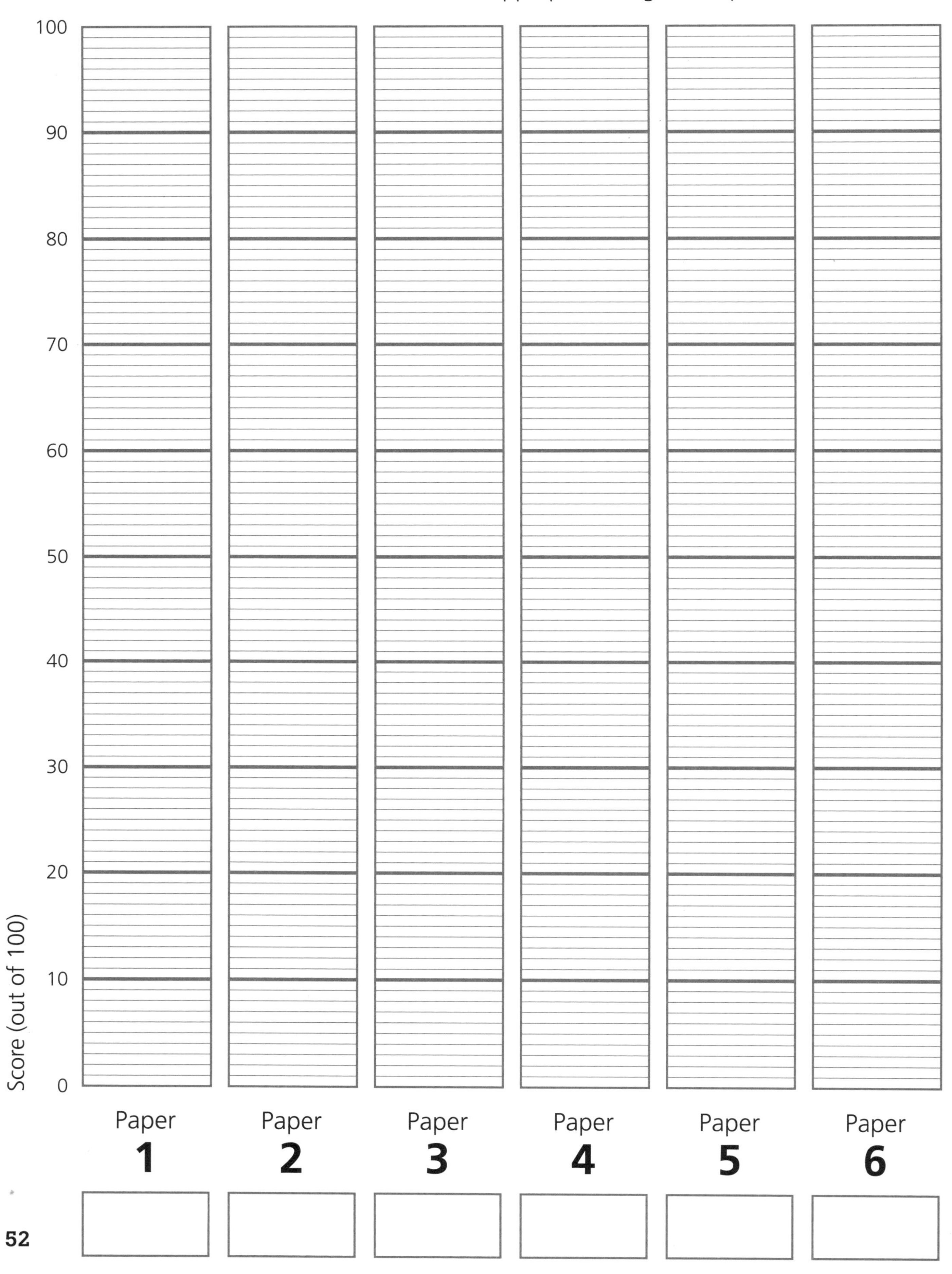